ROBERT LOUIS STEVENSON

Dr Jekyll and Mr Hyde

Retold by Stephen Colbourn

D1246398

HEINEMANN ELT

ELEMENTARY LEVEL

Series Editor: John Milne

The Heinemann ELT Guided Readers provide a choice of enjoyable reading material for learners of English. The series is published at five levels – Starter, Beginner, Elementary, Intermediate and Upper. At **Elementary Level**, the control of content and language has the following main features:

Information Control

Stories have straightforward plots and a restricted number of main characters. Information which is vital to the understanding of the story is clearly presented and repeated when necessary. Difficult allusion and metaphor are avoided and cultural backgrounds are made explicit.

Structure Control

Students will meet those grammatical features which they have already been taught in their elementary course of studies. Other grammatical features occasionally occur with which the students may not be so familiar, but their use is made clear through context and reinforcement. This ensures that the reading as well as being enjoyable provides a continual learning situation for the students. Sentences are kept short – a maximum of two clauses in nearly all cases – and within sentences there is a balanced use of simple adverbial and adjectival phrases. Great care is taken with pronoun reference.

Vocabulary Control

At **Elementary Level** there is a limited use of a carefully controlled vocabulary of approximately 1,100 basic words. At the same time, students are given some opportunity to meet new or unfamiliar words in contexts where their meaning is obvious. The meaning of words introduced in this way is reinforced by repetition. Help is also given to the students in the form of vivid illustrations which are closely related to the text.

Contents

A Note About the Author

Robert Louis Stevenson was born in Edinburgh, Scotland on 13th November 1850. He was a weak, ill child and he had no brothers or sisters.

Stevenson's father was an engineer and he wanted his son to be an engineer too. But Robert Louis Stevenson wanted to be a writer.

His first two books, written in 1878 and 1879, were about his travels in Europe. His most famous books were written when he was older.

In 1873, when he was 23, Stevenson became ill. He was never well again. Doctors told him that the cold, wet weather in Scotland was bad for him. So in 1876 he went abroad – to France. While he was there he met an American woman, Fanny Van de Grift Osborne. Robert and Fanny fell in love. Fanny had two children and she was separated from her husband.

In 1879, Stevenson followed Fanny to California, USA. Fanny got divorced from her husband and she married Robert in San Francisco in 1880.

The Stevenson family travelled to many countries. They lived in England, France and Switzerland as well as in the United States.

In 1889, they moved to the island of Samoa in the South Pacific. Stevenson died there on 3rd December 1894. He was 44 years old.

Treasure Island was published in a children's magazine in 1883. This exciting adventure story made Stevenson famous. *The Strange Case of Dr Jekyll and Mr Hyde* and *Kidnapped* were published in 1886. *Dr Jekyll and Mr Hyde* is one of the most popular mystery stories that has ever been written. Many films have been made of it. Other books are: *The Master of Ballantrae* (1889) and *Catriona* (1893). Stevenson died before he finished writing *Weir of Hermiston*.

A Note About the Story

Dr Jekyll and Mr Hyde is a story which takes place in London in 1885 and 1886. London was the largest city in the world at that time. It was a centre of industry and also a great port.

In 1885, there were no cars in the streets of London. Carts and carriages were pulled by horses. Cabs were taxis pulled by horses. There were no telephones at that time and people sent messages in letters. The streets of London were lit at night by gas lamps. There were no electric lights until the beginning of the twentieth century.

In this story, Henry Jekyll is a rich and clever doctor who lives in the centre of London. He has a large house and many servants. He does not have to work because he is rich. He spends his time studying science and medicine in his laboratory.

The People in This Story

Dr Henry Jekyll

Mr Edward Hyde

J. G. Utterson

Mr Enfield

Dr Lanyon

Sir Danvers Carew

Poole, a servant   **Maud Doyle,** a servant

Mr Maw, the chemist

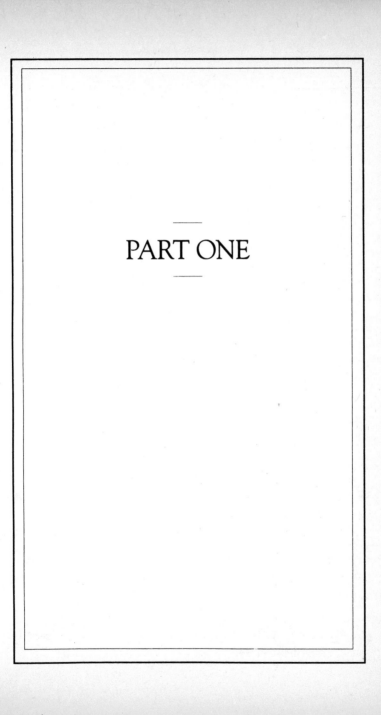

PART ONE

1

The Door

Mr Utterson was a lawyer. In the year 1885 he was fifty-five years old. He was a tall, thin man. His face was pale and the colour of his hair was silver. He always wore a white shirt and a black suit. These were the clothes of a lawyer. He lived alone in a large house near the centre of London.

Mr Utterson was a serious man who did not smile very often. But he was kind and intelligent and had many good friends. Most of his friends were doctors or lawyers. They liked Utterson because he listened carefully, but said very little. And Utterson always helped his friends.

Every Sunday, Utterson met his friend, Mr Enfield. The two men liked to go walking in London together. Enfield showed Utterson many new and interesting places.

One Sunday afternoon, Enfield took Utterson to the East End of London. This was a poor part of the city, but there were also many interesting markets and shops in the East End. People from different countries lived there. On weekdays it was a lively and busy place. However, on Sundays, the markets and shops were closed and the streets were empty.

Enfield took Utterson down a narrow street. Here the houses were old and dirty. Some of them were empty and some had broken windows. Utterson did not like this street.

'Why did you want to come here?' Utterson asked.

Enfield stopped. He pointed at an old door on the other side of the street.

*Enfield stopped. He pointed at an old door on the
other side of the street.*

'Look at that door,' said Enfield.

Utterson looked at the door. It was black and dirty. It was the door to an old house. Above the door there was one window. The house was next to a dark courtyard.

'I want to tell you a strange story,' said Enfield. 'My story is about that door.'

Utterson looked at the door while Enfield told his story.

'A few days ago,' said Enfield, 'I stayed overnight with friends, not far from here. Then, early the next morning, I started to walk home. But I did not know this part of London and I lost my way. I walked along this street. I wanted to find a cab so that I could ride home.'

'And did you find a cab?' asked Utterson.

'No, I didn't,' Enfield replied. 'But I saw a very strange man.'

'A strange man? What was strange about him?' asked Utterson.

'It's difficult to describe him,' Enfield continued. 'I saw him walking quickly along the street. He was coming towards me, on the other side of the street. He was a small man. His hat was pulled down so I could not see his face.'

'And what was strange about that?' asked Utterson.

'There was nothing strange – at first,' said Enfield. 'But I also saw a young girl running along a side street. She was about ten years old. She was not looking where she was going. She was running very fast and she ran into the strange man.'

'So, what happened?' asked Utterson.

'The man knocked her over,' said Enfield. 'Then he kicked her. She was lying in the street and crying loudly. He walked away.'

12

'And what did you do?' asked Utterson.

'I shouted at him,' said Enfield. 'I ran across the road – over there.' He pointed towards the old door. 'I stopped the man. I took hold of his arm and pulled him back. I wanted him to help the girl.'

'And did he help her?' asked Utterson.

'No. He said nothing and did nothing. He didn't understand what he had done,' Enfield continued. 'People came out of their houses when they heard the child crying. Her father came out of his house and took her indoors. One of the neighbours went to get a doctor.'

'Was the girl injured?' asked Utterson.

'No, she wasn't injured,' said Enfield, 'but she was very frightened.'

'And did this strange man speak to the girl or her father?' asked Utterson. 'Did he say he was sorry?'

'No, he didn't,' said Enfield. 'He was very quiet. He did not care about the child. The people around us were very angry, but he said nothing.'

'How strange!' said Utterson. 'Tell me, what did this man look like?'

13

'That was the strangest thing about him,' said Enfield. 'His face was ... ordinary. I can't describe it easily. Perhaps his face was rough or ugly. There was nothing unusual about it. But there was something evil in that face. When I looked at that man, I thought of a wild animal!'

'Evil? A wild animal?' said Mr Utterson. 'Surely your description can't he true?'

'I am telling you the facts,' said Enfield. 'The man had hurt someone and he did not care. The man was very quiet. But the girl's father was very angry and shouted to his neighbours, "Get the police!"'

'Then the man became worried.'

'Did anyone get the police?' asked Utterson.

'No,' Enfield continued, 'the strange man looked at the girl's father.

'He said, "Don't call the police. I'll pay you money. How much do you want?" '

'What did the girl's father say then?' asked Utterson.

'I spoke first. The girl's family was poor,' said Enfield, so I said, "A hundred pounds!" '

'A hundred pounds!' said Utterson in surprise. 'That's more money than the father could earn in a year. Did the strange man pay?'

'Yes, he did, and he got the money from over there.' Enfield pointed at the old door on the other side of the street.

'The man went to that door,' he said. 'I followed him. The man opened the door with a key.'

'What did you see inside the house?' asked Utterson.

'I saw a pleasant room,' said Enfield. 'There was an expensive red carpet on the floor. In the middle of the room there was a long table and only one chair. The man went to the table and took a cheque book from a drawer. He sat down and wrote a cheque for one hundred pounds.

'He said, "Take this cheque to Coutts Bank. The bank will pay one hundred pounds in cash." '

'And is that the end of the story?' asked Utterson.

'No. Not quite,' said Enfield. 'I looked at the cheque. There was a name printed on it. But the name on the cheque and the man's signature were different.'

'Had he stolen the cheque book?'

'No, he hadn't. The man saw that I was looking at the cheque.

'He said, "The bank will pay the money. Come with me to the bank. I will show you."

'And so I went to the bank with the man and the girl's father. I gave the cheque to the bank cashier. He looked at the signature on the cheque carefully. He looked at the bank records. He read some information about the bank's customers. Then he paid the money in cash. And now the girl's family is a hundred pounds richer than before.'

'That's strange,' said Utterson. 'What was the name printed on the cheque and what was the signature?'

'The name printed on the cheque was Dr Henry Jekyll,' said Enfield. 'But the signature was – Mr Edward Hyde. The bank has special instructions. Mr Hyde can sign Dr Jekyll's cheques.'

'Really? That is most unusual,' said Utterson. 'So, the strange man's name is Mr Hyde.'

'You seem very surprised. Do you know the names?' asked Enfield.

'I know Henry Jekyll,' said Utterson, 'but I do not know Edward Hyde.'

2

Mr Hyde

Enfield had finished his story. Utterson was silent and thoughtful as they left the East End. The two men did not speak as they walked back towards the centre of the city.

Utterson was thinking about the unusual story. He was thinking about Dr Jekyll and the strange Mr Hyde. He said goodbye to Enfield and went home.

Utterson lived near the centre of London. His house was close to Oxford Street. One room of the house was his office. In his office, he kept all his important papers and documents in a strong, metal safe.

He went into the office and opened the safe with a key. There were many papers and documents inside. He took out a brown envelope. Inside the envelope was a legal document – a will. It said what would happen to someone's property when they died. Utterson looked after people's wills because he was a lawyer.

This will was written in neat handwriting. Dr Jekyll had written it himself.

These are the wishes of Dr Henry Jekyll:

When I die, all my possessions, money and property will go to my friend, Edward Hyde.

If I disappear for more than three months, Edward Hyde will look after all my money and property.

Henry Jekyll   *Henry Jekyll*   *19th January 1885*

Utterson had been a friend of Henry Jekyll for a long time. He did not like this document.

'Why have I never met Edward Hyde?' he asked himself. 'Who is Edward Hyde? Why does Henry Jekyll want to give all his property to Edward Hyde?'

Utterson decided to talk to another friend called Dr Lanyon. Lanyon had known both Henry Jekyll and Utterson for many years. He lived nearby, in Cavendish Square. Utterson walked to Dr Lanyon's house and knocked on the door.

'Come in, come in,' said Dr Lanyon. 'How are you? Tell me all your news.'

Dr Lanyon had thick white hair. He was an old man but he still looked young. He was always happy and lively.

'Have you seen Henry Jekyll in the past few weeks?' asked Utterson.

'No, I haven't,' Dr Lanyon replied. 'I have sent him many invitations to dinner. But he is always busy in his laboratory where he does his scientific work. I think I have made him angry. He told me about his scientific work and I said it was nonsense. He has some strange ideas. His ideas are not scientific. I do not believe his work will be successful.'

'I do not know anything about his scientific work,' said Utterson. 'I am Henry Jekyll's lawyer. I am not a doctor or a scientist. But, tell me, have you heard of a man called Edward Hyde? He is a friend of Henry Jekyll.'

'No,' said Dr Lanyon. 'I've known Henry Jekyll for ten years, but I've never heard of Edward Hyde.'

Utterson thanked Dr Lanyon and went home. That night, he thought about Edward Hyde. Who was this mysterious man? Why did Henry Jekyll want to give all his money to Edward Hyde? Why did Jekyll let Hyde use his cheque book?

———

All next day, in his office, Utterson thought about Edward Hyde. 'Who is this man?' Utterson asked himself again and again.

That evening, he went to the East End of London again. He found the narrow street where he had walked with Mr Enfield. He found the old black door where Enfield had seen Edward Hyde. He waited near the door for an hour. He wanted to see if Edward Hyde came to this house. But no one entered or came out of the old door.

The next evening, Utterson went there again. He walked up and down the street for an hour, but he saw no one.

On the following evening, Utterson went to the street in the East End once more. He walked up and down the street. Then he waited in the entrance to the courtyard near the old door. The street was empty. He saw no one. He waited and waited. Then, at last, he heard footsteps and looked out of the courtyard entrance. On the other side of the street, a small man was walking quickly towards him.

The man put his hand in his pocket and took out a key. He walked across the street and stopped in front of the old door.

Utterson came out from the entrance to the courtyard. He looked carefully at the man. He could see the man's face in the light of a street lamp. It was an ordinary face, but Utterson did not like it. He was sure that this was the man Enfield had seen.

*It was an ordinary face, but Utterson
did not like it.*

'Mr Hyde?' Utterson asked.

The small man did not look at Utterson. 'That is my name,' he said in a low voice. 'What do you want?'

'I am a friend of Dr Henry Jekyll,' said Utterson.

'You won't find him here,' said Mr Hyde. 'How do you know who I am?'

'Dr Jekyll told me about you,' said Utterson.

'He never told you,' said Mr Hyde. 'You're lying!'

Utterson was angry. His face became red. Mr Hyde opened the old door quickly. He disappeared into the house and locked the door behind him. Utterson was now standing in the street alone.

'I shall know your face again, Mr Hyde,' he said to the locked door. 'I shall remember your face.'

But what did Mr Hyde's face look like? Utterson could not describe him easily. Hyde was small and his face was pale. His clothes were too large for him. He spoke in a low, rough voice. The man looked evil, Utterson decided. How could this man be a friend of Dr Jekyll? Did Hyde know a secret about Dr Jekyll? Was Hyde using this knowledge to harm Dr Jekyll?

Utterson went in a cab to Dr Jekyll's house. It was a large house, near Cavendish Square. An old servant called Poole opened the door.

'Good evening, Poole,' said Utterson. 'Is Dr Jekyll at home?'

'I think he went out, sir,' said Poole. 'Will you wait a moment? I'll go and see if Dr Jekyll is in his laboratory.'

Utterson waited in the hall. He looked at all the expensive furniture and paintings around him. Dr Jekyll was a rich man. The house was very large and had many rooms. Utterson knew that Jekyll's laboratory was at the back of the house, but he had never seen it.

There were several servants in the house who cooked and cleaned. Poole had worked for Dr Jekyll for many years. He knew Dr Jekyll very well and looked after him.

'I'm sorry, sir. Dr Jekyll is out,' Poole said when he returned. 'He often goes out by the laboratory door at the back of the house. I heard the door close, but I didn't see him leave.'

'I saw Mr Edward Hyde this evening,' said Utterson. 'Tell me, Poole, does Mr Hyde often visit Dr Jekyll?'

'Yes, he does, sir,' answered Poole. 'Mr Hyde comes in by the laboratory door. I don't see him, but I hear his voice. Mr Hyde is a good friend of Dr Jekyll. All the servants do everything Mr Hyde asks.'

'Does he come here when Dr Jekyll is out?' asked Utterson.

'Yes, sir. Mr Hyde has a key,' said Poole. 'He works in the laboratory.'

'And you do not see him?'

'No, sir. He speaks to me from inside the laboratory. He doesn't open the door.'

'Thank you, Poole,' said Utterson. 'Good night.'

'Good night, Mr Utterson.'

3

Dr Jekyll

Two weeks later, Dr Jekyll had a dinner party. He invited a few of his friends to his house near Cavendish Square. He invited Dr Lanyon and Mr Utterson, as well as several other people.

Dr Jekyll was a rich man. So he did not have to earn any money. He spent all his time studying medical and scientific problems in his laboratory.

The guests ate a good dinner. Dr Jekyll talked and laughed. But he did not talk about his work. All the guests enjoyed themselves. At twelve o'clock, all the guests said good night and left, except for Utterson.

Utterson stayed because he wanted to talk to Dr Jekyll.

'Jekyll,' he said, 'I'd like to talk to you about your will.'

Dr Jekyll was a large man, aged fifty, with a smooth and handsome face. He sat back in a chair by the fire. He looked at Utterson.

'Utterson,' said Dr Jekyll, 'you worry too much. You are the same as Lanyon. He worries about my scientific work. You worry about my will.'

'Yes. I have told you that I do not like your will,' said Utterson.

'Yes,' said Dr Jekyll, 'you have told me several times.' He was angry.

'I have heard about Mr Edward Hyde,' said Utterson.

Dr Jekyll was no longer angry. His face became worried. 'What have you heard about Edward Hyde?' he asked.

'I have heard nothing good about him,' said Utterson.

22

'You are the same as Lanyon,' said Dr Jekyll. 'He worries about my scientific work. You worry about my will.'

'He is not a bad man, really,' said Dr Jekyll. 'I ask you to believe me. Remember, if I ... disappear ... Edward Hyde will look after everything for me. All my money and property will go to Edward Hyde. He will take everything. You must make sure he gets everything.'

Utterson was silent.

'You are my lawyer as well as my friend,' said Dr Jekyll. 'You must promise to do this for me. I cannot tell you why, but it will help me. I am worried. Please make sure Edward Hyde receives all my property. Please promise to do this for me.'

Utterson sighed. Then he said, 'Very well, I promise. I will make sure that Mr Edward Hyde receives all your property.'

Dr Jekyll smiled.

4

The Murder of Sir Danvers Carew

In October 1885, Mr Utterson received a message from a police inspector. The inspector asked Utterson to come to the police headquarters at Scotland Yard. Utterson went to Scotland Yard early in the morning.

'Thank you for coming so early in the day,' said the police inspector to Utterson.

'That's all right,' said Utterson. 'How can I help you?'

'There has been a murder,' said the inspector.

'Who has been murdered?' asked Utterson.

'We do not know the dead man's name,' the inspector replied. 'But he was carrying a letter addressed to you. So we think that you know him. Can you identify the body for us?'

Utterson's face became pale.

'Show me the body,' he said. 'I will tell you the man's name if I know it.'

'Very well, sir. Please follow me,' said the inspector.

Utterson followed the inspector to the mortuary. This was the place where the police put the bodies of murdered people. The bodies were identified by friends or relatives.

There was a body lying under a white sheet in the mortuary. The inspector pulled back the sheet and showed Utterson the dead man's face.

'I know him,' said Utterson. 'He is Sir Danvers Carew. He is a famous doctor.'

'Thank you, sir,' said the inspector.

'You said that he was carrying a letter addressed to me,' said Utterson. 'Do you know what happened? Who murdered Sir Danvers? Where? Why?'

'I have a statement from a witness,' said the inspector. 'I'll show it to you.'

The inspector took Utterson back to his office. He showed him a document.

**METROPOLITAN POLICE
SCOTLAND YARD**

Statement of: *Maud Doyle*
Date: *15th October 1885*
My name is Maud Doyle. I am a servant. I work for Mr Parker and I live in Mr Parker's house on the corner of Regent Street and Cavendish Square. My room is at the top of the house and I can see into Cavendish Square.

Last night, at about 11 o'clock, I went to my room. I remember that the moon was shining brightly. I looked out of my window and saw the corner of Cavendish Square.

There was only one person on the street. An old gentleman with white hair was walking towards Cavendish Square. He was well-dressed and he had something in his hand – a paper or a white envelope.

Then I saw another man walking towards the old gentleman. This second man was small. He carried a walking stick in his hand. I had seen this man before. I think he lives near here. He came to Mr Parker's house once with a message from Dr Jekyll. I remember the man because I was afraid of him. I do not know why I was afraid of him. I remember his name. He is called Mr Edward Hyde.

The old gentleman stopped Mr Hyde and spoke to him. He showed him the paper in his hand. Perhaps he was asking for directions to an address .

Mr Hyde suddenly became very angry. I could not hear what he said, but he lifted his walking stick. The old gentleman seemed surprised and started to move away from Mr Hyde. But Mr Hyde hit the old gentleman with the stick. The gentleman fell down and Mr Hyde hit him again on the head. He hit him so hard that the walking stick broke.

I did not see any more because I fainted and fell down on the floor. When I was able to stand up, I looked out of the window again. The old gentleman lay in the street. I could see blood coming from his head. I called Mr Parker. He sent someone to get the police.

Signature of: Maud Doyle   *Maud Doyle*

Witnessed by: Inspector Samuel   *J. D. Samuel*

'So, that's what happened,' said Utterson. 'Your police-men found that Sir Danvers was dead.'

'Yes,' said the inspector. 'They also found the letter Sir Danvers was carrying. It was addressed to you. That's why I asked you to come here this morning. We also found half of a broken walking stick.'

'I see,' said Utterson.

'Do you know Mr Hyde?' asked the police inspector.

'I met Mr Hyde, once,' said Utterson.

The police inspector showed the broken walking stick to Utterson. 'Could this be Mr Hyde's walking stick?' he asked.

Utterson suddenly felt cold and ill. He had seen the walking stick before. He had given it to Dr Jekyll for his fiftieth birthday.

'I do not know if this is Hyde's stick,' he said. 'But I can take you to the place where Mr Hyde lives.'

The police inspector sent for a cab, then he and Utterson went outside. The cab arrived and Utterson gave directions to the cab driver.

'Take us to the East End,' he said. 'I will tell you where to go.'

It was a cold autumn day. The air was thick with fog and the London streets looked grey.

Utterson gave directions to the narrow street where he had seen Mr Hyde. He pointed to the old door.

'That is where Mr Hyde lives,' he said to the inspector.

'Open up,' shouted the inspector, knocking on the old door.

The window opened upstairs. A woman with a red face and red hair looked out at them.

'He's gone,' she said. 'What do you want?'

'Are you the owner of this house?' asked the inspector. 'I want to see inside. I'm a policeman.'

'He's in trouble, is he?' asked the woman, smiling. 'I'll open the door. What's he done?'

She came downstairs and opened the old door. Utterson and the inspector went inside.

'You want Edward Hyde, do you?' asked the woman. 'He paid me rent to live in these two rooms on the ground floor. Late last night he came here and gave me some money. He said he was going away – to France, perhaps.'

Utterson and the inspector looked around the two rooms. The rooms had expensive furniture in them and

Utterson and the inspector looked around the
two rooms.

were untidy. There were clothes on the floor. drawers were open. There were some burnt papers in the fireplace. The other half of the walking stick was behind the door. There was blood on it.

'Hyde is the man we want,' said the inspector. 'Hyde is the murderer of Sir Danvers Carew. We must find him and arrest him. We will search everywhere for Mr Edward Hyde.'

5

The Letter

Utterson went to Dr Jekyll's house near Cavendish Square. Poole, the servant, opened the door.

'Dr Jekyll thought you would come this morning, Mr Utterson,' he said. 'He's in the laboratory. I'll show you the way.'

Utterson followed Poole to the back of the house. He had never been into Dr Jekyll's laboratory before. It had no windows. Light came from gas lamps in the ceiling. There were shelves around the walls with bottles of chemicals on them. The chemicals were many different colours. There was a large wooden table in the middle of the laboratory.

Dr Jekyll was sitting behind the table. His face was pale. He looked ill. In front of him was a tall chemical apparatus made of glass. There were glass tubes which went into jars. There was a flame burning under one of the tubes. Green liquid was boiling in this tube. Dr Jekyll was examining the green liquid that dripped from the apparatus into a bottle.

'Have you heard the news?' asked Utterson. 'Your friend Edward Hyde has murdered Sir Danvers Carew.'

'Yes,' said Dr Jekyll. He did not look at Utterson. 'Poole told me the news. He heard it from people in Cavendish Square.'

'And where is Edward Hyde?' asked Utterson.

'I don't know. He has gone away. I don't know where – perhaps to France,' Jekyll said, in a tired voice. He continued to examine the green liquid.

'You aren't hiding him, are you?' Utterson asked.

'No, no,' Jekyll said quickly. 'He has gone away, I'm sure. He sent me this note.'

Dr Jekyll took a piece of paper from a drawer and showed it to Utterson.

Jekyll

I have done a terrible thing. You will hear the news very soon. I must leave London at once. The police are after me. But I will escape from them. I will leave the country on the next boat from Dover. I will go abroad to France or Italy. You will never see me again.

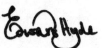

Edward Hyde

'Where was this note posted?' asked Utterson. 'Where is the envelope? Does it have a postmark? The postmark will show us where and when the note was posted. Surely it was written only a few hours ago? How was it delivered so quickly?'

'The envelope did not have a postmark. Somebody delivered the note early this morning,' said Jekyll nervously. 'I did not keep the envelope. In fact, I think I burned it.'

'I must tell the police,' said Utterson. 'They can send a message to the police in Dover. They must stop Edward Hyde before he gets on a ship.'

Jekyll nodded his head. He said nothing.

'And tell me,' Utterson continued, 'why did you leave all your money and property to Edward Hyde in your will?

Dr Jekyll took a piece of paper from a drawer and showed it to Utterson.

Did he say he would harm you?'

Jekyll nodded his head again. 'Yes,' he said quietly.

'I thought so,' said Utterson. 'He is a terrible man. He wanted to harm you! I'm sure he wanted to murder you. Why did you not tell anyone? You must tell me the whole story later. Now I must go to the police. Good day.'

Utterson left Jekyll in the laboratory and went to the front door. Before he left the house, he spoke to the servant, Poole.

'Tell me, Poole, who delivered a message to Dr Jekyll this morning?'

'There have been no messages, sir,' said Poole. 'No one has come to the door.'

Utterson thought that this was strange. Jekyll had said that Hyde's message was delivered early in the morning.

Utterson did not go to the police immediately. He had had an idea. Utterson thought that he recognized the handwriting in the note.

He went back to his house and opened the metal safe in his office. He took out Henry Jekyll's will. The will was written in Dr Jekyll's handwriting.

Utterson looked at the will. Then he examined the letter from Edward Hyde. He felt cold.

'The handwriting is the same!' he said.

6

Dr Lanyon

Mr Utterson told the police that Edward Hyde was going to Dover. He told them that Hyde was going to go to France. But the police did not catch Edward Hyde.

Three months passed. Friends of Sir Danvers Carew – the murdered man – offered a reward. They would give a thousand pounds for information about the murder. But no one had seen Edward Hyde since the night of the murder.

Utterson saw Dr Jekyll at New Year. Dr Jekyll looked happy, although his face was still very pale. He had a dinner party on 8th January for all his friends. He invited Dr Lanyon as well as Utterson and several other people. All the guests were happy and Jekyll talked and laughed. Perhaps he had forgotten Edward Hyde and the murder of Sir Danvers Carew? Utterson was pleased to see that his friend was happy again.

But that happiness did not last. Four days later, on 12th January, Utterson visited Dr Jekyll's house. Poole, the servant, opened the door.

'I'm very sorry, Mr Utterson,' said Poole, 'but Dr Jekyll will not see anyone.'

'Is he ill?' asked Utterson.

'He is working very hard,' said Poole. 'He has moved into the laboratory. He eats and sleeps there. I leave his meals outside the door.'

Utterson was worried. He left Dr Jekyll's house and walked round the corner to Cavendish Square. He wanted to talk to Dr Lanyon about Jekyll.

The last time he had seen Lanyon, on 8th January, Lanyon had looked fit and well. Now he looked like a very old man. He was ill and sad.

'I do not have long to live,' said Lanyon. 'I have had a terrible shock.'

Utterson did not know what to say. He did not want to believe that his good friend was dying.

'I think Jekyll is ill as well,' Utterson said. 'Have you seen him?'

'I never want to see that man again,' said Dr Lanyon.

'But, why?'

'Ask Jekyll,' said Lanyon.

'He will not see me.'

'I'm not surprised. Now, please leave me. I am ill and tired. Goodbye.'

Utterson left Dr Lanyon's house and went home. He was worried. He sat down and wrote a note to Dr Jekyll.

Dear Jekyll

   You are always busy when I come to your house. Do you know that Lanyon is ill? Have you seen him? I want to visit you and talk to you. Please tell me when I can come.

   Utterson   *Utterson*

A reply came from Dr Jekyll the next day.

My Dear Utterson

   I am sorry to hear that Lanyon is ill. He and I had a disagreement.

   Lanyon is an old man. He did not want to believe new ideas. He did not believe in my scientific work. He did not believe that my work was successful. But I showed him that it was successful. He became angry. He told me to leave his house and never return.

   You and I are friends, but please do not try to visit me. I am very busy. My scientific work is taking all my time.

   Your friend   *Henry Jekyll*

   Henry Jekyll

A week later, Dr Lanyon died. Utterson went to his funeral and saw many friends, but Henry Jekyll was not there.

Utterson was Dr Lanyon's lawyer. He took care of Dr Lanyon's will. Dr Lanyon had left all his money to his relatives. Then Utterson took out all the private papers that Lanyon had left in his desk. With the papers there was an envelope marked: *Private. For J. G . Utterson*.

He opened the envelope. Inside it there was a second envelope marked: *Read this after the death of Dr Henry Jekyll*.

Utterson was surprised. He wondered what was in the envelope. But he did not open it. He put the envelope into the safe in his office.

7

The Window

The next Sunday, Utterson went for a walk with his friend, Enfield. They walked towards Dr Jekyll's large house near Cavendish Square.

'Well,' said Enfield, 'we have not seen Mr Hyde again.'

'And we have not seen Dr Jekyll either,' said Utterson.

They looked at Jekyll's house. A window on the first floor was half open. Sitting at the window was Dr Jekyll.

'Jekyll!' Utterson called up to him. 'How are you?'

Dr Jekyll looked down at the two men sadly. 'I am very tired and weak,' he said. 'I will not live long.'

'You stay indoors too much,' called Utterson. 'Come out with us. Come for a walk. You need some fresh air and exercise. It will do you good.'

'I would like to come,' said Jekyll. 'But it is impossible. I cannot leave the house.'

'Then talk to us for a few minutes,' Utterson replied. 'You can stay there and we shall stand here.'

'Yes,' said Dr Jekyll smiling. 'I would like that.'

Suddenly Jekyll stopped smiling and put his hands to his face. He covered his eyes with his hands. His mouth was open. He did not speak to Utterson and Enfield. He shut the window and quickly turned away.

For a moment, Utterson thought he saw a different face at the window. It was not the face of Dr Jekyll. Then Jekyll turned away and was gone.

Utterson looked at Enfield in surprise. Enfield looked worried. But he said nothing. The two men walked on.

*Suddenly Jekyll stopped smiling and put
his hands to his face.*

8

The Last Night

A few days later, Dr Jekyll's servant, Poole knocked loudly on Utterson's door. Poole was frightened.

'What's the matter?' asked Utterson. 'Is Dr Jekyll ill?'

'I don't know, sir,' said Poole, 'but something is wrong.'

'Tell me what has happened.' said Utterson.

'Dr Jekyll has locked himself in his laboratory,' said Poole. 'He won't speak and he won't open the door.'

'Has he fallen?' Utterson asked. 'Perhaps he is unable to open the door himself.'

'I don't think so, sir,' said Poole. 'He has written notes and pushed them under the door.'

'And what do these notes say?'

'They all say the same thing, sir. They all ask for a special chemical. I've been to every chemist's in London. Every time I bring some of the chemical, Dr Jekyll says it's no good. He's sent me three times to Mr Maw the chemist with a note. Last time I went, Mr Maw became angry. He threw the note at me and told me not to come again.'

'Do you have the note?' asked Utterson.

'Yes, sir, here it is,' said Poole.

Mr Maw   13th February 1886

You sent me some of the chemical a few days ago. But it did not work. Please, please find me some of the chemical that I bought from you last year. I need it urgently. This new chemical is no good. Please, I beg you. Do not refuse to help me.

Henry Jekyll M.D.   Henry Jekyll MD

'And when did you last see Dr Jekyll?' asked Utterson.

'I … I'm not sure, sir.'

'Not sure! When did he go into his laboratory?'

'Nearly a week ago, sir. But, today, when I came back from Mr Maw the chemist, the laboratory door was open.'

'So, you saw Dr Jekyll today?'

'I saw someone,' Poole said in a low voice. 'Someone was in the old store room next to the laboratory.'

'Who?' asked Utterson.

'The man had white bandages round his head, so I couldn't see his face,' said Poole. 'But I don't think it was Dr Jekyll. It was a small man. The man ran back into the laboratory as soon as he saw me. That's why I decided to speak to you, Mr Utterson.'

'I see,' said Utterson. 'We must go to the house at once. I will speak to Dr Jekyll.'

Utterson put on his coat and went out with Poole. They walked quickly to Dr Jekyll's house.

All of Dr Jekyll's servants were standing in the hall. They were frightened. One of the servants was crying.

'Mr Utterson, sir, please help us,' she said quickly. 'The man has been shouting for Poole. He wants a special chemical.'

'Who has been shouting?' asked Utterson.

'The man in the laboratory,' said the servant.

'Not Dr Jekyll?'

'It's not his voice, sir.'

'Poole,' said Utterson, 'is there an axe in the house? We must break down the door of the laboratory.'

Poole got an axe and followed Utterson. Utterson walked to the back of the house. He listened carefully at the laboratory door. He heard someone walking up and down inside the laboratory. He heard a man's voice. The man was talking strangely.

'Jekyll?' Utterson shouted. 'Open this door!'

'Utterson!' A voice came from the other side of the door. 'I beg you to leave me in peace. Please, leave me alone.'

'That's not Dr Jekyll's voice,' cried Utterson. 'That's Mr Hyde! Break down the door, Poole.'

Poole swung the axe at the door. It cut into the wood. A scream came from inside the laboratory. The old door was strong. It took more than a minute to break it down. There was silence from inside the laboratory.

Utterson looked through the broken door. He could not see anyone inside the room. There was some white powder on a table. Utterson walked to the table and stopped.

A body lay on the floor behind the table. It was the body of a small man. The clothes the man was wearing were too big for him. The man was dead. There was a green bottle in his hand. The label on the bottle said 'Poison'.

'This is the body of Mr Edward Hyde,' said Utterson. 'He has killed himself with poison. Poole, get the police. I think that Mr Hyde has also killed Dr Jekyll.'

Poole went to get the police. Utterson looked around the laboratory. On Dr Jekyll's desk there was an envelope marked: *For Mr John Gabriel Utterson from Dr Henry Jekyll.*

Utterson picked up the envelope. The handwriting was Dr Jekyll's. But where was Dr Jekyll himself?

*A body lay on the floor behind the table. It was
the body of a small man.*

PART TWO

9

Dr Lanyon's Story

That evening, Utterson sat alone in his house. The police had taken away the body of Edward Hyde from Dr Jekyll's house. Now they were looking for Dr Henry Jekyll himself. None of his servants had seen him for a week.

Utterson had two documents to read. One was in the envelope from Dr Jekyll. The other was from Dr Lanyon.

He took Dr Lanyon's envelope from the safe. It was marked: *Read this after the death of Dr Henry Jekyll.* Utterson thought that Henry Jekyll was dead. So he opened Dr Lanyon's envelope and read the document.

Cavendish Square
London   *10th January 1886*

Utterson
   I have had a terrible shock. You will not believe me, but I will write this down. Yesterday I received a strange letter from Dr Jekyll. This is what he wrote:

Dear Lanyon
   You are my closest friend. I know we have disagreed in the past, but I beg you to help me now. I cannot go to my laboratory myself. Please do not ask me why. I need a chemical for my scientific work and I need it very urgently.
   Please, go to my house. My servant, Poole, will open the laboratory for you. Look in my medical

---

cabinet on the wall. Look in the drawer marked 'E'.
Inside the drawer there is a glass jar filled with
white powder. Please take this jar to your house. A
messenger will come for the jar at midnight.
Please help me.

Your friend   Henry Jekyll

I read the letter twice. I did not know what to think.
Was Jekyll mad? Why could he not go to his own house?

I did what he asked. I went to his house and showed
the letter to Poole. Then we went to the laboratory
together. Inside the laboratory, I found the drawer marked
'E' and took out the jar of white powder. After that, I
returned to Cavendish Square and waited for Jekyll's
messenger.

At midnight a small man came to the door. He was a
strange man. His clothes were too big for him and he
spoke in a low voice.

'Are you from Dr Jekyll?' I asked.

'Yes, I am. Have you got it?' the man asked. 'Have
you got the chemical that Jekyll wants? Where is it?'

I did not want to invite the man into my house. But I
said, 'Come in.'

'Where is it?' the small man asked again.

'On the table, over there,' I said. 'Take it.'

The man took the jar of white powder and sighed. He
looked at the white chemical in the jar and smiled.

'Do you have a glass and some water?' he asked.

I pointed towards my desk. There were glasses and a

jug of water on a tray. The small man put some of the
white powder and a little water into a glass. The liquid
bubbled and became bright green.

The man looked at me. His face was evil.

'You would not believe me, Lanyon,' he said. 'Now,
look.'

I did not know what he meant. I had never seen this
man before.

The man drank the liquid in the glass and gave a loud
cry. He put down the glass and held on to the table. Was
he in pain? Then, suddenly, he began to change. I stood
up and moved towards the door. I did not believe what I
saw and I was afraid. I wanted to leave the room. I
wanted to run out of the house and call for help. But I
could not move. I watched the horrible change in the
man's face.

The man's face changed slowly. His body became
larger. He leaned over the table. Then he stood up and
looked at me. I was terribly afraid.

The man had become taller. His face had become
smooth and handsome. It was not the face of the man who
had come to my house. I saw a different face – one that I
had known for many years. I saw the face of Henry
Jekyll!

'You did not believe me, 'said Jekyll. 'I told you about
my work in my laboratory. You said my ideas were
nonsense. Now you can see that you were wrong. You did
not know the man who came to your house this evening.
That man's name is Edward Hyde.'

'I know the name of Edward Hyde,' I said. 'Hyde is a

*The man drank the liquid in the glass and
gave a loud cry.*

murderer. The police are looking for him. I do not want to see him in my house again. And I do not want to see you either.

'Go back to your laboratory. I do not want to know what you do there. Now, leave my house and never come back.'

Jekyll left my house. I never want to see him again. This has been a terrible shock. I do not think I will live much longer. Now I know that Dr Jekyll and Mr Hyde are the same man

H. Lanyon   *H. Lanyon*

PART THREE

Henry Jekyll's Statement

Utterson finished reading Dr Lanyon's document and put it down on the table. He did not know what to believe. Utterson had known Lanyon for many years. He did not think Lanyon was mad. But was Lanyon's story true? Utterson was sure that Lanyon had seen something very terrible. But were Jekyll and Hyde the same man?

There was one other document to read – this was from Jekyll's laboratory. It was in Dr Jekyll's handwriting.

Utterson,

You know I have spent many months in my laboratory. I'm sure you want to know about my work. What have I studied? What have I learnt?

I have studied many drugs and chemicals. I have taken drugs to control my body and my mind.

You will want to know why. Did I take the drugs for pleasure, as some men do? No. There was a serious reason.

There is both good and evil in all of us. The mind has both a dark and a light side. I have tried to separate these two parts of the mind. I wanted to separate the dark, evil part of my mind from the good, light part. I wanted to remove the evil from my mind. I wanted to be completely good. And I have succeeded. I have found a way to separate good from evil.

I tried many drugs. I almost killed myself. At last I made the right drug. But I was not sure. I had to try it. Perhaps the drug would kill me. But I had to know.

Late one night in my laboratory, I drank the drug. The drug was a bright green liquid.

I was alone and afraid. I waited for a moment, then the drug began to work on my body. I felt sick. There was a terrible pain in my chest. I could not breathe. I could not stand up. I cried out and held on to the table. Then I fell down and lay on the floor for some time.

When, at last, I stood up. I felt different. The pain had gone. I felt young and strong again.

There is a mirror in the laboratory. I went to the mirror and looked at my face. My face had changed. I touched it. It was my own face. But I was a new man.

I did not know that I had made a different man. His name is Edward Hyde. He is the bad part of me.

I separated good from evil by using the drug. Edward Hyde is the evil part of me. He is completely evil. When he was inside me, the good part of me could control him. When he was separate from me, I could not control him.

Now, I cannot control him any longer. He comes to me more and more often. He takes my body and uses it. I cannot stop him. He is evil. I cannot control him.

I see through his eyes. I think with his thoughts. They are terrible thoughts. He thinks of cruelty and murder. I see him hitting that old man again and again with his stick – with my stick. I cannot forget the blood.

Only one drug can control him. I bought the chemical to make the drug from Mr Maw the chemist's. But there

'I went to the mirror and looked at my face.'

was something unusual about Mr Maw's chemical. The same chemical from other chemists does not work. Only Mr Maw's chemical can save me.

But Mr Maw does not have any more of his special chemical. Now I cannot control Edward Hyde. This is the last letter I will write as Henry Jekyll.

Soon Edward Hyde will come again and take my body and my mind. I have locked myself in my laboratory.

Edward Hyde cannot go outside because the police are looking for him. And I cannot go outside, because I am both Henry Jekyll and Edward Hyde.

There is only one answer. I shall take poison. If I kill myself, I will also kill Edward Hyde.

Henry Jekyll

POINTS
FOR
UNDERSTANDING

Points for Understanding

1

1 What was Mr Utterson's job?
2 What did Utterson look like?
3 Why did Utterson's friends like him?
4 Where did Enfield take Utterson?
5 Enfield saw a man knock over a young girl.
    (a)   What did the man do after he knocked over the girl?
    (b)   What did Enfield do?
6 'Tell me, what did this man look like?' asked Utterson.
    What did Enfield tell Utterson?
7 The strange man said he would give money to the girl's father.
    (a)   Where did the man go to get his cheque book?
    (b)   What was strange about the cheque that he wrote?
8 Enfield told Utterson two names. Why was Utterson surprised?

2

1 Utterson got Henry Jekyll's will out of his safe. What did the will say?
2 What did Dr Lanyon think about Dr Jekyll's scientific work?
3 Did Dr Lanyon know Mr Hyde?
4 Why did Utterson go back to the street in the East End?
5 Utterson could not describe Edward Hyde easily. What did he remember about this strange man?
6 What did Dr Jekyll's servant, Poole, tell Utterson about Mr Hyde?

3

1 Who did Henry Jekyll invite to his dinner party?
2 Most of the guests left at midnight. Why did Utterson stay?
3 What did Dr Jekyll look like?
4 What did Utterson promise Dr Jekyll?

4

1 Why did the police inspector ask Utterson to go to Scotland Yard?
2 How did Sir Danvers Carew die?
3 Why did Maud Doyle know the name of the murderer?
4 Why did Utterson suddenly feel cold and ill?
5 What did Utterson and the police inspector find in Hyde's rooms?

5

1 Describe Dr Jekyll's laboratory.
2 Dr Jekyll showed Utterson a note. Who was it from and what did it say?
3 Jekyll told Utterson that the note was delivered early in the morning. How did Utterson find out that Jekyll was lying?
4 Utterson looked again at Dr Jekyll's will. What did he find out?

6

1 Did the police catch Edward Hyde?
2 What happened on 8th January?
3 Why wouldn't Dr Jekyll see anyone?
4 What did Dr Lanyon tell Utterson?
5 Utterson wrote a letter to Dr Jekyll. What did he ask him?
6 Jekyll wrote a letter to Utterson. What did he tell Utterson?
7 Utterson found an envelope with Lanyon's papers.
   (a)   What was inside the envelope?
   (b)   What did Utterson do with the envelope?

7

1 Where did Enfield and Utterson see Dr Jekyll?
2 What did Utterson invite Dr Jekyll to do? What was Jekyll's reply?
3 Dr Jekyll said he would like to talk to Utterson and Enfield. What happened next?

4 Utterson saw something strange at Dr Jekyll's window. What did he see?

8

1 Why did Poole come to see Utterson?
2 What did Dr Jekyll want from Mr Maw, the chemist?
3 Who did Poole see in the old storeroom?
4 Why were Dr Jekyll's servants frightened?
5 Poole broke down the door of the laboratory with an axe. What did Utterson see on the floor?
6 What did Utterson find on Dr Jekyll's desk?

9

1 Utterson had two documents to read.
    (a) Who were the documents from?
    (b) Which document did he read first?
2 Lanyon received a strange letter from Dr Jekyll. What did he ask Lanyon to do?
3 Who came to Dr Lanyon's house at midnight?
4 What did Lanyon's visitor do with the white powder?
5 What happened next?

10

1 'I have taken drugs to control my body and my mind,' wrote Jekyll. Why did he take these drugs?
2 Jekyll made a drug to separate good from evil. What happened when he drank the drug?
3 Who was Edward Hyde?
4 Jekyll said that he could not control Hyde any longer. How do you think Jekyll felt?
5 What happened to Henry Jekyll? Why?

A Christmas Carol *by Charles Dickens*
Riders of the Purple Sage *by Zane Grey*
The Canterville Ghost and Other Stories *by Oscar Wilde*
Lady Portia's Revenge and Other Stories *by David Evans*
The Picture of Dorian Gray *by Oscar Wilde*
Treasure Island *by Robert Louis Stevenson*
Road to Nowhere *by John Milne*
The Black Cat *by John Milne*
Don't Tell Me What To Do *by Michael Hardcastle*
The Runaways *by Victor Canning*
The Red Pony *by John Steinbeck*
The Goalkeeper's Revenge and Other Stories *by Bill Naughton*
The Stranger *by Norman Whitney*
The Promise *by R. L. Scott-Buccleuch*
The Man With No Name *by Evelyn Davies and Peter Town*
The Cleverest Person in the World *by Norman Whitney*
Claws *by John Landon*
Z for Zachariah *by Robert C. O'Brien*
Tales of Horror *by Bram Stoker*
Frankenstein *by Mary Shelley*
Silver Blaze and Other Stories *by Sir Arthur Conan Doyle*
Tales of Ten Worlds *by Arthur C. Clarke*
The Boy Who Was Afraid *by Armstrong Sperry*
Room 13 and Other Ghost Stories *by M. R. James*
The Narrow Path *by Francis Selormey*
The Woman in Black *by Susan Hill*

For further information on the full selection of
Readers at all five levels in the series, please refer
to the Heinemann ELT Readers catalogue.

Macmillan Heinemann English Language Teaching, Oxford

A division of Macmillan Publishers Limited

Companies and representatives throughout the world

ISBN 0 435 27317 5

Heinemann is a registered trademark of Reed Educational & Professional Publishing Limited

This retold version for Heinemann ELT Guided Readers
© Stephen Colborn 1995
First published 1995

Illustrated by Jolyon Webb
Typography by Adrian Hodgkins
Designed by Sue Vaudin
Cover by Brad Gary and Threefold Design
Typeset in 11.5/14.5 pt Goudy
by Joshua Associates Ltd, Oxford

Printed and bound in Turkey